It's another Quality Book from CGP

This book is for anyone doing GCSE Graphic Products.

It contains lots of tricky questions designed
to make you sweat — because that's the only
way you'll get any better.

It's also got the odd daft bit in to try and make
the whole thing at least vaguely entertaining for you.

What CGP is all about

Our sole aim here at CGP is to produce the highest quality
books — carefully written, immaculately presented and
dangerously close to being funny.

Then we work our socks off to get them out to you
— at the cheapest possible prices.

Contents

Published by Coordination Group Publications Ltd.

Contributors:

Victoria Brereton
Juliet Cash
Rhonda Dockray
Alan Rix

Alice Shepperson
Richard Smith
Claire Thompson
Chrissy Williams

With thanks to Lucy Workman for the proofreading.

ISBN: 1-84146-798-7
Groovy website: www.cgpbooks.co.uk

Jolly bits of clipart from CorelDRAW

With thanks to TECHSOFT UK Ltd for permission to use a screenshot from 'DESIGN TOOLS — 2D DESIGN'

Printed by Elanders Hindson, Newcastle upon Tyne

Design Brief

Q1 Explain briefly why companies carry out customer research.

Q2 Describe what a design brief is for and what it should include.

Q3 Each of the people or groups of people below have a problem. For each problem, write a one-sentence design brief for a product that might be able to help.

a) A boy has broken his finger in a beef grinding accident.
It is badly crushed in one place.

b) Ms Smith's bedroom is relatively tidy except for her dressing table, which is always covered in pots of make up.

c) The Jones family are constantly forgetting where they have put their keys.

Q4 Companies need to be aware of the existing market and existing products when they think about designing and manufacturing a new product. Give three reasons why companies might decide to introduce a new product into the market.

Q5 Explain the following terms in relation to Design and Technology.

a) identifying a need

b) gap in the market

c) consumer research

d) user group

Hello, Good Evening and Welcome...

Knowing the Design Process is half the battle with D & T. Make sure you know every stage of the process, what it's for, and what order the stages come in. After that, it should be a breeze...

Research

Q1 Research is used to get ideas before you start designing your product. Describe three things that you could aim to find out from your research.

Q2 There are two forms of research — primary and secondary. Primary research is when you collect information yourself and secondary research is when you use information collected by someone else. Say whether each of the sources of information below is primary or secondary.

a) Internet   e) newspapers

b) questionnaires   f) interviews

c) letters   g) magazines

d) books

Q3 The table below shows three different ways of carrying out primary research. Copy and complete the table using the sentences in the box to say how each one will help you design your own product.

Method of Research	Use
Questionnaires	
Disassembling an existing product	
Measuring an existing product	

Tells you about people's likes and dislikes. This will help you identify market trends and your target group.

Tells you how a current product is made and how it works. It will help you to decide which materials and processes you need to use and how your product will meet consumers' needs.

Gives you an idea of the weight, size and shape of your product and its sensory features.

Sensory analysis — finding out how a product feels, looks and smells

Chicken?

Q4 Once you have completed your research, you need to decide how to use the information you have gathered. What is the proper term for this stage of the design process?

Design Specification

Q1 Write a sentence to explain what a design specification is.

Q2 Think of as many factors as you can that could be included in a design specification. Draw a spider diagram to show your ideas.

Q3 The table below shows some of the features that should be included in a design specification. Copy and complete the table by matching the terms (in the box) with their meanings.

Term	Meaning
	how long will the product last
	concerns repair when product fails
	the measurements
	the product's job
	what shape, colour, texture, etc. will be most suitable

dimensions   durability   maintenance

aesthetics   function

Q4 Below is a list of specification points for different products. Write out the appropriate specification points for each product.

a) office lamp

b) cosmetic mirror

c) disposable lady shaver

d) computer mouse

must be ergonomically designed so that it is comfortable to hold and use

designed for a female, must be replaced after use

to be designed so that it is free standing and suitable for a professional environment

designed to be transportable, to fit in a pocket or bag

Q5 Write three points that could be included in the design specification for a CD rack.

Generating Proposals

Q1   Give a brief description of each of the following terms, and say how they might help you generate ideas for a design proposal.

     a)   mood board

     b)   brainstorming

     c)   an existing product

Q2   Designers use sketches to present their ideas. What is the proper term for labelling and adding notes to sketches?

Q3   Your notes should cover the size and shape of your design. Write down five other things that you could include in your notes in order to explain your ideas.

Q4   There are several different ways of presenting your designs. Choose three different ways, and give a brief description of each one. Write your answers into a table like the one below.

Presentation Technique	Description

Mood board — mine's black all over on a Monday morning...

This bit is kind of interesting. The main thing is to get as many different ideas flowing as possible. Then later you can go back and pick out the ones you really like, and forget the ones you don't.

Development

Q1   In order to develop a design it needs to be explored in detail. Give three features of a design that you could consider during the development stage of the design process.

Q2   It is helpful to produce models when you're developing your design. Give the proper name for a design model and write a sentence to explain why models are useful in the design process.

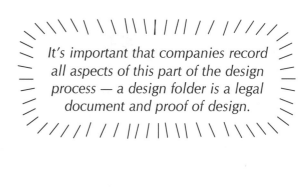

It's important that companies record all aspects of this part of the design process — a design folder is a legal document and proof of design.

Q3   Name three ways you could record how you have developed a design.

Q4   Use the words in the box below to complete the following sentences.

Once you have developed your designs using .... , models or tests, you need to .... the results. This will allow you to make .... to your design and improve the product, or make it ready for .... It is also important that the design is checked to ensure that it meets the ....

> design specification   mass production
>
> modifications   analyse   sketches

Evaluation

Q1 Name three ways of testing a product.

Q2 Imagine you have carried out a survey for people to test the product you have designed. Write down five standard questions that could appear in that survey.

Q3 Below are two similar products. Evaluate the two products on the aspects of function, appearance and ergonomics.

Product 1   Product 2

Q4 Copy and complete the following sentences using the words from the box below.

> manufacturing time   assembly process   cost
>
> production   materials   availability

There are a number of things designers need to know once they've finished developing their ideas:

a) The .... , tools and equipment that they will need, and their ....

b) How long it will take to produce each item — the ....

c) How much it will .... to manufacture each item.

d) The .... — the cheapest and most effective way of putting the product together. This will be important when planning for ....

Manufacturer's Specification

Q1   What is a manufacturer's specification?

Q2   Manufacturers' specifications are sometimes presented using working drawings. Explain what is meant by working drawings.

Q3   Name one way of presenting a costing sheet on a PC.

Q4   Below is a list of points that should be included in a manufacturer's specification. Copy and complete the sentences using the words from the box.

> tolerances   construction   dimensions   finishing
> costs   costings   quality control

a) Clear .... details — explaining exactly how each piece is going to be made.

b) .... — precise measurements of each part.

c) .... — the maximum and minimum sizes of each part.

d) .... details — any special sequencing for finishing.

e) .... instructions — where and how the manufacturing process should be checked.

f) .... — how much each part costs, and details of other .... involved.

__Planning Production__

Q1   Explain how charts might help you to plan the production process.

Q2   Describe what a Gantt chart is used for and how it works.

Q3   The graphical symbols below are used in flow charts. Copy them out and use
       the words on the right to show what stage of a flow chart they represent.

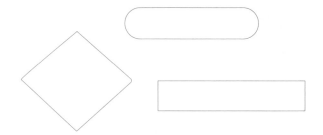

Process

Decision

Start / End

Q4   Describe what a summative evaluation is and what it involves.

Q5   Below are seven stages on how to tackle the exam. Draw a flow chart, putting
       the stages in the right order. Use the correct graphical symbols for each stage.

Do I have time left
(YES or NO) ?

Equipment needed — pen pencil,
ruler, rubber, sharpener

Turn up on time.

Read through the questions.

TIME UP

Answer the questions.

Check answers.

__You can make flow charts for virtually anything...__

...like making a cup of tea, for instance. You could even draw some accompanying designs, and annotate
them. And while you're drinking your tea, you might like to think about how you're going to hide your
designs and what you're going to say if someone asks you what you've been doing for the last two hours.

Paper and Board

Q1 Identify the three types of paper below.

a)

b)

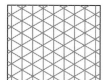

c)

Q2 What unit is the weight of paper and card measured in?

Q3 Give one use for each of the following two materials.

a) foam board

b) corrugated board

Q4 Give two reasons why most cardboard is environmentally friendly.

Paper is great

Board already? But you've only just started the section...

Look round the room and make a list of 10 products that are manufactured from paper and board. Write down what type of paper / board they're made of and how it's been used.

Plastics

Q1 Copy and complete the following sentences, using the words provided in the box.

There are .... groups of .... Thermoplastics is the group of plastics

that .... be remoulded. Thermosetting plastics .... be remoulded.

plastics	can	cannot	two

Q2 Copy out the following statements and say whether they're true or false.

a) Acrylic is a thermoplastic.

b) Plastics conduct electricity.

c) Covers for plugs are made from a thermosetting plastic.

d) Carrier bags are made of polythene.

e) You can bend plastic using a line bender.

f) PVC stands for polyvinyl cartons.

Q3 Complete the spider diagram below and brainstorm four other advantages of plastics.

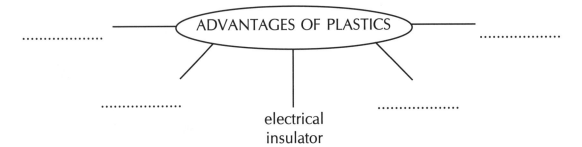

....   ADVANTAGES OF PLASTICS   ....

....   electrical insulator   ....

Q4 Identify the types of plastics the three products below are manufactured from.

a)

b)

Techno

mixed by DJ Vinyl

c)

Q5 Describe the main properties of the following plastics.

a) high density polyethylene (HDPE)

b) low density polyethylene (LDPE)

c) cellulose acetate

d) polyvinyl chloride

Plastics

Q1 Vacuum forming is ideal for producing packaging for trays, casings and containers (e.g. for chocolates). Explain, with the aid of diagrams, how the vacuum forming process works.

Q2 Identify the machine below and explain how it works, stating what materials you could use on it.

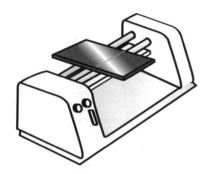

Q3 Suggest the process most likely to be used to manufacture each of the following products.

a)

drinks bottle

b)

school chair

c)

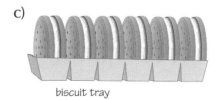

biscuit tray

e)

drain pipe

d)

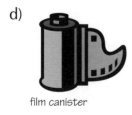

film canister

Smart Materials

Q1   Describe what a smart material is.

Q2   List four stimuli that some smart materials can respond to.

Q3   Give one example of a product that each of
the following smart plastics are used to make.

It was the staff ball, and everyone was in their smartest
material, including Dave in his little lycra number.

a) electro-luminescent panels

b) lenticular plastic

c) liquid crystal display (LCDs)

d) polycaprolactone (polymorph)

Q4   What two materials make up the alloy Nitinol?

Q5   The information below is about smart wire.
Fill in the missing gaps using the words in the box.

Nitinol is an alloy that exhibits shape .... It can be made to .... a particular

shape or .... and return to it when a particular .... or .... is applied.

> remember   temperature
>
> memory   length   voltage

Q6   Give two uses of Nitinol smart wire.

__Smart Materials__

Q1   Give three examples of stimuli that smart dyes respond to.

Q2   Copy and complete the following table to show what each
smart dye responds to and what it can be used to produce.

Dyes	Stimulus	Product
photochromic dyes	light	
solvation-chromic dyes		nappies, hankies and hygene products
		bubble bath, baby spoons, dishes and wine bottle labels
thermochromic liquid crystal		

Q3   Describe how Peripheral Interface Controllers (PIC's) work, and what they can be used for.

Q4   Match the names of modern materials from the box to their descriptions below.

Lycra   teflon   carbon fibre
             optical fibres   modified enzymes

a) Biological materials — ....

b) Strong material — ....

c) Material for communication technology — ....

d) Material for finishing processes — ....

e) Materials for insulation and clothing — neoprene and ....

Fillers and Finishing

Q1   We finish materials to protect them from damage, preserve them and enhance their appearance. Explain how you would finish the following materials using the tools and equipment listed below.

  a) wood   b)   metal   c)   plastic

> wet & dry paper   glass paper
>
>   file
>
> emery cloth   buff and polish
>
>   Brasso   varnish

Tip — one of these can be used on all three.

Q2   Copy and complete the table below to show what different sorts of filler can be used for.

Filler	Use
Polyfilla	
plaster of Paris	

Q3   Name two types of solvent commonly used to make paint.

Buff and polish — reminds me of my days as a nude house cleaner...

Make sure you know which fillers and finishes are best for which surfaces. Be kind to our metal pals. And make sure you don't overdo any of them, or you'll have none left.

Drawing and Painting Media

Q1   What is gouache, and what is it used for?

   a) a type of Hungarian stew

   b) a type of opaque paint used for flat areas of colour and highlights

   c) a South American cowboy

Q2   Pencils are classified by their hardness and softness.
      Which pencils would be used for precise technical graphics?

Pencil use No.34:
faking madness

Q3   Describe what these graphical terms mean:

   a) rendering

   b) sketching

   c) typefaces

Q4   Airbrushing is a technique used by many designers.
      Give one reason why airbrush drawings tend to be so expensive.

Q5   Suggest an alternative method that you can use to easily
      produce airbrush effects, and give a specific example.

Q6   Why aren't water-based pens suitable for large, flat areas of colour?

Drawing and Painting Equipment

Q1   Write down the names of the graphical tools below.

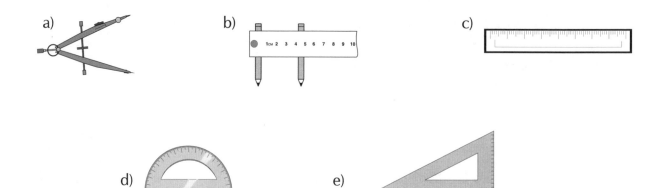

a)

b)

c)

d)

e)

Q2   Copy out the table below. Explain how each piece of equipment in question 1 would be used.

Equipment	Use
a)	
b)	
c)	
d)	
e)	

Q3   Name one piece of drawing equipment which is essential for oblique projections.

Q4   Draw the following graphical instruments and describe the difference between them.

a) French curve

b) flexi curve

Adhesives

Q1   Describe what an adhesive is.

Q2   What does PVA stand for?

Q3   What materials is PVA used with?

Q4   For each of the four adhesives below, write down
one material that the adhesive could be used on.

a)
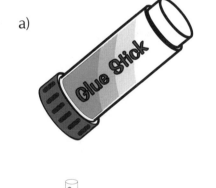

b)

c)

d)

Q5   Name two safety precautions you should take when using adhesives.

Don't come unstuck — learn all about glue...

Always make sure surfaces are clean of dirt, dust, oil and moisture before you start gluing
anything — that way, things are more likely to stay stuck together.

Cutting Tools

Q1 For each material on the spider diagram below, add three suitable cutting tools.

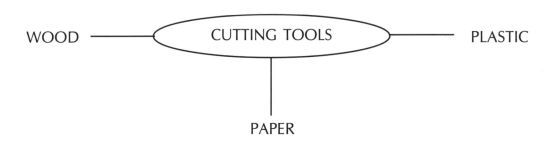

Q2 The picture below is of a pair of pinking shears.
Explain what they would be used for.

Q3 Look at the list of materials below and match each one with the tools that can be used to cut them.

1) paper

2) styrofoam

3) MDF

4) corrugated card

craft knife

scissors

hot wire cutter

coping saw

Q4 Explain why you would use a steel rule with a craft knife instead of a plastic ruler.

Q5 Suggest two safety precautions you should take when working with MDF.

Q6 Suggest appropriate tools for cutting a circle out of a thick piece of card.

Tools and Materials

Q1   Below are descriptions of three different saws used to cut wood.
Give the name for each saw that has been described.

a) This small saw can be used to cut wood and plastic in curved or irregular shapes.

b) This saw is good for sawing thick material along a straight line.

c) This is an electrical version of a coping saw or piercing saw. It can be used on plastics.

Q2   Suggest one material you could use wet and dry paper on.

Q3   What is a vacuum former used for?

Q4   Give the name of the machine in the picture.

Q5   Copy and complete these sentences.

a) A twist-drill bit is used to create ....

b) A needle file is used on ....

c) Files come in a variety of shapes and sizes. They are used to ....

Fixings

Q1 Fixings are used in product assembly.
Briefly describe what is meant by the term 'fixings'.

Q2 Draw and describe three ways you can join card
together. Remember to label your diagrams.

Q3 What fixing would you use in cardboard engineering to create a moveable joint?

Q4 For each joint, say which ones are permanent and which are non permanent.

a)

b)

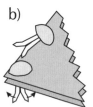

c)

d)

Q5 For each joint, give an example of the product it could be used on.

a) paper clip   d) velcro

b) paper prong fastener   e) press stud

c) staples   f) glue

A page about fixes, glue and joints, eh? Sounds a bit dodgy to me...

Now then, now then — there are loads of ways of joining materials together, just make
sure you think carefully about which method is most appropriate for the thing you're making.

Ways of Producing Work

Q1 Write down five functions of a dead fancy photocopier.

Modern photocopiers can
make things smaller.

Q2 What would you use a light box for?

a) storing lanterns

b) transporting soft furnishings

c) tracing an image

Q3 Describe briefly what DTP is.

Q4 Write down the industries from the box below where DTP could be used.
For each one, give an example of what they might use it for.

> news office   computer department   publishers
>
> building site   hospital reception
>
> furniture department store   supermarket

What Designers Do...

Q1 Name four ways a designer can communicate an idea.

Q2 Advertising is a massive industry nowadays. Name four ways a product can be promoted.

Q3 Below are two terms a designer may use. Describe what is meant by each term.

a) produced to scale

b) mock-up

I mocked this up using polystyrene.

Yeah, I can tell. It looks rubbish.

Q4 Before companies launch a new product, they need to find a gap in the market.

a) Describe what is meant by "gap in the market".

b) Describe how this might affect product designs.

Buy my carrots.

Spud was not a natural carrot salesman.

Q5 Name two things that might influence what a customer chooses to buy.

What do designers do? — er... design...

Glad we've got that sorted, because it means I can sleep tonight, and I won't have to stare at the walls in a cold sweat, lower lip trembling, and wishing I had devoted more of my life to D & T.

Sketching

Q1 Copy and complete the sentences below about sketching, using the words from the box below.

.... drawing is where you use a pen or a pencil and nothing else. It's a good way of

getting your ideas down on .... because it's very ....

2-D freehand sketches are useful because they show a great deal of .... ,

and .... drawings show how the object will look as a whole.

> 3-D   paper   freehand   quick   detail

Q2 Describe what is meant by the term 'crating'.

Q3 Find a 3-D object that's made up of both rectangular shapes and circles, e.g. a camera, a pencil sharpener, or something like that.

a) Sketch accurately in 2-D a front view of the object, using boxes and circles to start you off.

b) Draw an accurate 3-D view of the object, using crating.

Q4 Below are three types of lines. Identify which is vertical, which is horizontal and which is egg-shaped.*

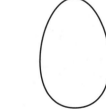

*N.B. This is a particularly hard question, so don't spend too long on it if you don't know the answer.

Sketching

Q1 Draw a square-based pyramid, starting by drawing a cuboid.

Q2 Sketch three cubes, each using a different drawing type as listed below.

  a) one-point perspective

  b) isometric

  c) oblique

Q3 In CAD, it is possible to view objects in <u>wireframe</u>.
Describe what this term means, and why you might want to use this technique.

Q4 This is a photo of a pond and alien.
Sketch the view as shown, and label the
alien and the riverbank using arrows.

Enhancement — Shading

Q1 Draw the shapes below using your pencil. Decide where the light source is coming from, then shade in the shapes accordingly.

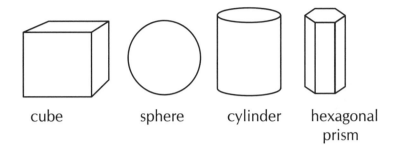

cube   sphere   cylinder   hexagonal prism

Q2 In your own words explain what rendering means (in relation to drawings, not buildings).

Q3 One way of shading an object is to use lots of dots.

    a) Name a kind of printer that uses this method.

    b) Give one disadvantage of using dots to shade by hand.

Q4 Why might a designer choose a soft pencil to shade a drawing?

Q5 Describe a method you could use to achieve each of the following effects using only a soft graphite pencil:

    a) showing different colours on different faces of an object

    b) giving the impression of solidity

    c) showing that a surface is very shiny

3B felt a warm glow inside at the thought of cute fluffy lambs gamboling in the fields.

26

Enhancement — Surfaces and Textures

Q1   Copy this drawing of a cuboid. Using coloured pencils, shade it in so that it looks like a block of timber. (Tip — think about where the end grain will go.)

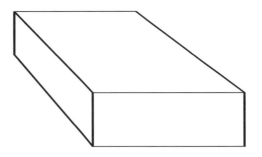

Q2   Below are some products made of different materials. Suggest appropriate colours and types of pencil you could use to shade in each of the different materials if you were drawing them.

Q3   Define the following graphical terms.

opaque   gloss

transparent   texture

Q4   Suggest an appropriate technique for drawing each of the following:

a window

a pale-coloured ceramic mug

a textured metal file

Enhancement — Colour and Mood

Q1 Copy and complete the colour wheel on the right by labelling the blank segments with the correct colour.

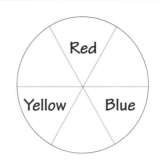

Q2 The colours in the wheel above can be divided into two groups — primary and secondary.

    a) Say which group each of the colours in the wheel belongs to.

    b) Describe the difference between primary and secondary colours.

    c) Describe what is meant by the term "complementary colours".

Q4 Colour can have a big effect on the 'look' of a product. Say what colour you think each of the products below would be, giving reasons for your answers.

 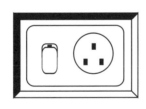 

Q6 The 'Thunder Looper' was a very tall roller-coaster at Alton Towers. The top of it was painted dark green. Give a possible reason why this was done.

Q7 Write down the colour(s) best suited to representing the products below.

> *a hi-tech product*   *an environmental product*   *a fun, child-like product*

Enhancement — Colour in Print

Q1 Copy and complete the following sentences about television screens, using some of the words in the box below — you might need some of them more than once.

1) .... pictures are made up of thousands of coloured .... known as pixels.

2) TV pictures consist of three colours; ...., ... and ....

3) Each .... consists of a .... green and blue bar or dot. The colour you see on the screen depends on the .... of each of these bars (or dots).

> television   blue   black   pixel   green   red
> yellow   intensity   dots

Q2 Some printers use CMYK colours to print images. What do these initials stand for?

Brian was a little surprised to find the loose strand of cotton in his pants was actually a dragon.

Q3 Name the printing process used to produce T-shirts.

Q4 Dpi is a term used in printing. What does "dpi" stand for?

Q5 Describe the process of creating colour using screen printing.

C for cyan, M for magenta, Y for yellow and, of course, K for black...

There are two different 'sets' of colours: subtractive and additive. Paints and inks use <u>subtractive colour</u>: the primary colours are red, yellow and blue, and they mix together to make black. But light uses <u>additive colour</u>: the primary colours are red, green and blue, and they mix together to make white. Make sure you know which is which, and where each each is used.

Paper Sizes, Mounting and Fixatives

Q1 Put the paper sizes in the circles below in the correct order, starting with the largest.

Q2 Sketch a landscape page and a portrait page.
Give an example of something each one is used for.

Q3 Describe how you would manufacture a simple booklet.
Present your answer in three steps or bullet points.

Q4 The statements below are about how to make a mount to frame a picture.
Put the following instructions in the correct order.

1) Cut a hole in the middle of the card.

2) To protect your picture, spray a fixative over it to stop it smudging or fading.

3) Get a piece of card of an appropriate size to fit your picture.

4) Place the hole slightly higher than the middle of the picture.

Q5 The cover of a booklet is supposed to protect the pages, but it's usually the cover that gets worn away first. Give one method of protecting a booklet's cover from wear and tear.

CAD/CAM

Q1 Once a product has been designed using CAD, the information is sent to machines that then make the product. Say what this process is called.

    a) RAM (Random Access Memory)

    b) CAM (Computer-Aided Manufacture)

    c) SHAM (Superconducting Heat-Aspirated Metaphysics)

Q2 The table below shows three products that need text incorporated into their design. Copy and complete the table by describing a style of font that would be suitable for each product.

Product	Font style
birthday card for an old woman	
wrapper for new fun frog chews	
poster advertising a conference for catwalk models	

Q3 Name five products that would need text incorporated into their design.

Protecting Paper Products

Q1 Describe why it might be necessary to protect a paper product.

Q2 Give three examples of paper products that may need protecting.

Q3 The tool pictured on the right is a laminator.

a) How does a laminator help to protect paper products?

b) Briefly describe how a laminator 'laminates'.

Q4 Other than to protect them, why are photographs and names in passports, driving licences and identification badges encapsulated?

Q5 Newspapers and magazines are sometimes encapsulated to ensure that inserts don't fall out. What is this sort of encapsulating called?

Q6 Laminating machines can give two different kinds of finish to a product. Name the finishes and describe their appearance.

It was a gruesome Matt finish

Yes, find the laminator — it will preserve this page forever..

This is important stuff. Do you know what happens to paper when it's not protected?
It's not a pretty sight at all. Everything just goes horribly, horribly floppy.

Recording Stages Using Photography

Q1 Photographs can be used at different stages of the design process.
Say how photographs can be used to help at each of the stages listed below.

1. research

2. design

3. testing

Q2 Give two advantages and two disadvantages of using a digital camera, rather than a regular 35mm camera. Copy and complete the table below to show your answers.

Advantages	Disadvantages

Q3 Designs with photographs on tend to be more expensive than those without. Give a reason why you think this may be so.

Q4 You can change and experiment with digital images using computer software. If you were designing a hand-held games console on a computer, name three things that you could change about your pictures with an art package.

Smelly cat, smelly cat, it's not your fault you're not an experimental digital image that's been made using computer software and then evaluated — la lala la la...
Take photos of equipment you can't remember the name of, or products you think have a good design. Print them off and evaluate them, like carrying out a product analysis. That's what I did. Got kinda hooked too. You might call product analysis my social life, I suppose.

Summary — Communicating Ideas

Q1   Give a definition of each of the design terms listed below.

Design Term	Definition
sketching	1.
light source	2.
two-dimensional	3.
three-dimensional	4.
hatching	5.
solid fill (CAD term)	6.

Q2   The table below shows the colours chosen for different products.
Suggest a reason why the colour was chosen for each product.

Colour	Product	Reason for Colour
white	toilets	1.
red	heater on vacuum former	2.
black	solicitor's chair	3.
green	recycling bins	4.
silver	widescreen TV	5.
pink	teddy bear	6.

Q3   The table below contains groups of words. Name a product that each could be linked to.

Groupings	Products
'cartridge', 'recycled', 'graph'	
'pritt stick', 'PVA', 'photo mount'	
'Times New Roman', 'Arial', 'Bauhaus 93'	
'laser', 'inkjet', 'deskjet'	
'satin', 'gloss', 'matt'	

Pictorial Drawings

Q1   Copy the sentences below and fill in the gaps using words from the boxes.

Perspective drawing can be used to draw .... objects. It shows a ....

of an object. First you must draw a .... line and then .... points.

vanishing		realistic view
	3-dimensional	horizon

Q2   There are two types of perspective commonly used —
one-point and two-point perspective. Draw a cube in
one-point perspective below the horizon line.

oops... wrong book...

Q3   When drawing an object in two-point perspective the view varies
according to whether it's drawn above, on or below the horizon line.
Copy and complete the sentences below, matching parts a), b) and c)
to their correct endings.

a)   When a cube is drawn above the horizon line you can see...

b)   When a cube is drawn on the horizon line you can see...

c)   When a cube is drawn below the horizon line you can see...

i)   ...the sides and the top.

ii)   ...the sides and the bottom.

iii)   ...only the sides.

Get it right — or I'll poke your 2-point perspectives out...

Isometric drawings can be accurate and to scale, but perspective drawings give a more realistic view of
objects — and 2-point is more realistic than 1-point. Learn that, and it'll help you get valuable marks.
It might also help you avoid all those embarrassing pictorial drawing dilemmas in later life.

More Pictorial Drawings

Q1 Isometric drawing is another technique used to draw
3-dimensional objects. List three rules for drawing in isometric.

Q2 What is the main difference between isometric and perspective drawing?

Q3 Which of the following statements refer to isometric drawing and which refer
to perspective drawing? Organise your answers in a table like the one below:

Objects are drawn at 30°.

Objects appear to get smaller in the distance.

You can draw a 3-dimensional view of the object that only shows the sides.

Objects can be drawn to scale.

Objects can't be drawn to scale.

Use grid paper or a set square to draw objects.

Isometric	Perspective

Q4 Draw the isometric shapes below in two-point perspective below the horizon line.

a)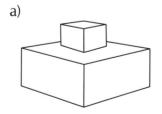
b)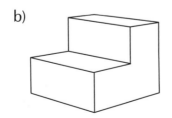
c)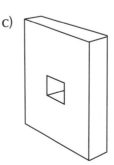

Working Drawings

Q1 Copy and complete the sentence below using words from the box.

Orthographic drawings show .... views of a .... object. The views are

drawn .... to .... The most common method of orthographic drawing

is .... angle. The front, ... and end view of an object are drawn.

plan	3-dimensional	accurately
2-dimensional	3rd	scale

Q2 Draw the symbol for 3rd angle orthographic projection.

Q3 Copy and complete the table below to show the British Standard recommendations on lines.

Where to use this line	Line
outlines	
projection / construction lines	
hidden detail	
dimension lines	

Q4 What is an exploded drawing?

Q5 What is a sectional drawing?

Q6 Plan views are always drawn to scale. Match up the following ratios to what they represent.

a)   Scale 1:2   i)   The drawing is twice the product's actual size.

b)   Scale 2:1   ii)   The drawing is half the product's actual size.

c)   Scale 1:1   iii) The drawing is one hundredth of the product's actual size.

d)   Scale 1:100   iv)   The drawing is the same size as the object.

Surfaces, Nets and Boxes

Q1 Name the three 3-D objects that can be made from the following nets.

a)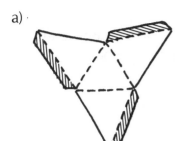

b)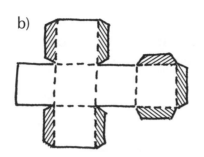

c)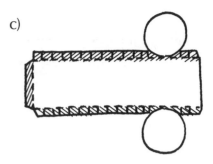

Q2 Copy and complete the following sentences using the words in the box below.

When drawing nets, all lines which are to be cut should be .... lines.

Dotted lines should be used to represent .... and areas to be glued should be

.... or hatched.

> solid   folds   shaded

Q3 When designing a box, what is a 'tuck-in base'?

Q4 Give two advantages of using an automatic base for a box used in a fast food restaurant.

Q5 Name a CAD/CAM machine that you could use to design and cut out your nets accurately.

Graphs and Charts

Q1 Name a type of graph or chart that can be used to show data clearly by using a series of equally spaced columns or bars.

Q2 Pictographs use symbols or pictures to represent information. Copy and complete the following table to show the number of ice creams sold each month throughout the summer.

Month	Number of Ice Creams Sold	Pictograph
May	100	▽ ▽
June	250	
July	300	
August	350	
September	125	

Q3 Pie charts represent data by dividing a circle or pie into portions. Say which of the following the whole pie adds up to.

a) 10%   b) 20 pieces
c) 1000 slices   d) 100%

Q4 Produce a pie chart to show the following data about the popularity of different holiday destinations.

Destination	Number of Holidaymakers
Spain	20
America	17
Canada	12
France	30
Greece	16
Other	5

Q5 Both bar charts and line graphs show the relationship between different factors, but this data is displayed in different ways. How is a line graph different from a bar chart?

My favourites are steak and kidney pie charts...

Make sure you know the differences between all the charts and graphs. Learn what each one does, and what it's most useful for. Then it's Marks'r'us for you and me, baby.

Labels, Icons and Ideograms

Q1   What is an <u>enactive</u> label?

Q2   Iconic labels appear on your computer screen. Copy and complete the
sentence below using the words in the bubble to explain what they're used for.

Iconic labels are used as .... to files, folders or .... They can be easily ....

and are usually .... in all software packages. The user would be able to ....

identify what they are for.

programs   similar
shortcuts   easily
identified

Q3   Ideograms can be used instead of writing.
Suggest what the ideograms below could be used for.

a)    b) 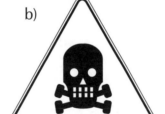   c)

Q4   When designing your own label, which of the following
rules should you follow? Write out the sensible answers.

Keep it simple.

Make sure the symbol is appropriate for the thing you are labelling.

Use an appropriate colour.

Always try to include some unfamiliar symbols.

Try not to use any words.

Make sure it can be reproduced.

Q5   What does the colour red usually represent on a symbol or label?

<u>Branding</u>

Q1   Pictures, words and symbols are on many products we buy, to show the make or brand, like in the pictures below. Give three other examples of places where you might see examples of branding.

Q2   What does corporate identity mean? Pick the correct answer from the choices below.

   a) A logo, symbol or style used to identify one product or
      company from other similar products or companies.

            b) A type of hairstyle which all company workers must have.

               c) A police line up.

                  d) The uniform some workers might wear.

Q3   Why do companies often use a simple picture to create their corporate identity?

Q4   Copy and complete the following sentence using words from the box below.

   When designing a .... identity, companies need to consider who

   they're aiming to .... and where the corporate identity will ....

   It must be able to be .... easily to many different surfaces

   in order for it to retain its ....

attract	appear	impact
corporate	transferred	

Flow Charts and Sequential Illustrations

Q1   Flow charts are used to show a series of events in a process. Each event has a different shaped box. What are each of the following shapes used for?

Q2   Draw a flow chart with eight stages, including the four stages below, to show how to boil an egg. Remember to include a start point and an end point.

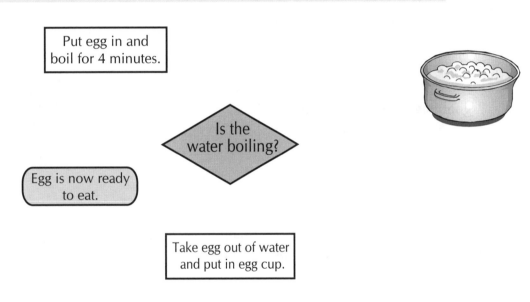

Put egg in and boil for 4 minutes.

Is the water boiling?

Egg is now ready to eat.

Take egg out of water and put in egg cup.

Q3   Produce a flow chart using the correctly shaped boxes to show how to paint a front door. You must put an undercoat and a top coat of paint on and allow time for the paint to dry.

Q4   What is a sequential illustration, and when might you use one?

How to boil an egg — step 1: find a chicken...

This stuff really just boils down to common sense. Boils... ahaHAHAHAhaha hum... *sigh* Anyway...
Flow charts and sequential illustrations are step-by-step instructions for doing any task — not difficult to do, and they can make things much much easier for the person you're writing them for, so worth getting right.

Why People Buy a Product

Q1   What is a well-designed product? Copy and complete
the sentence using the words from the box below.

A .... product successfully carries out

its .... and .... consumers.

> well-designed   function
>   attracts

Q2   What is a well-manufactured product? Copy and complete
the sentences using the words from the box below.

A well-manufactured product is made to a ....

and is .... to the .... design.

> good standard   original
>   accurate

Q3   Consumers choose to buy products for different reasons. Give three
different reasons why a particular product might be bought.

Q4   Explain why it is important that manufacturers
know what consumers think about their product.

Q5   List three factors that manufacturers must consider when trying to sell a product.

Well at least Charlie and Tim don't eat beans...

Charlie **A**nd **T**im **B**elched **A**fter **F**ood. Learn that phrase to help you remember the five things
that consumers and manufacturers look for when buying or designing a new product:
Cost, **A**esthetic appeal, **T**ime of assembly, **B**rand loyalty, **A**dvertising and **F**ashion.

Evaluation

Q1   State four reasons why a product must be evaluated after completion.

Q2   State three ways of recording results during the
design and manufacture of a product.

Q3   Why is it important to record information during the design and manufacturing process?

Q4   What is quality control? Choose the words from
the box below to work out the missing words.

Quality control is the .... evaluation process that

.... the quality of a product during the .... process.

This ensures it is produced to the .... standard possible.

monitors	ongoing	
	highest	manufacturing

Q5   The picture below shows a mould made from MDF. The mould is designed to make a
desk tidy. The mould is to be put into a vacuum forming machine. Suggest three checks
that could be made to ensure the plastic mould is made to the highest possible standard.

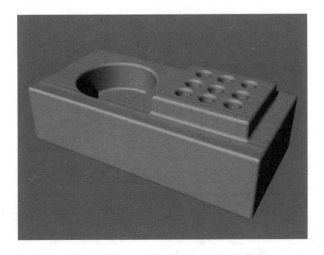

Evaluation

Q1 When evaluating a product it's important to compare it with the original design specification. List five other points that could be checked when evaluating a product.

Q2 What is a "target audience"?

Q3 You have just made a new type of squeaky toy for dogs. Write down four questions that you could use on a questionnaire, aimed at your target audience, that would enable you to improve your product. (By target audience I mean the owners, not the dogs...)

Q4 Say which of the following sentences are true and which are false:

a) Questionnaires are designed to get information from consumers.

b) Questionnaires ask consumers about their habits and preferences.

c) To get the most accurate results, only a small number of people should be questioned.

d) Different types of people should be questioned.

Q5 What is a focus group?

Q6 After completing a graphics project you decide to evaluate it using a questionnaire. Name three ways in which you could then **visually communicate your findings** from the questionnaire.

I spend my days evaluating the quality of Eastenders...

It's up and down and all over the place — changing actors and plots quicker than you can say "The Queen Vic". Well, evaluating <u>products</u> is a tad more useful. Make sure you get all this stuff learnt. It's fine to MAKE a product, but you need to find out what people think about it too.

Moral and Cultural Issues

Q1   Below are a number of social and environmental considerations
      to take into account when selecting materials, components and
      manufacturing processes. Copy and complete the table below
      to give an example of each. I've done the first one for you.

Consideration	Example
Could the use of the product or material harm someone?	Paints or materials could be toxic.
Could the manufacturing of the product harm someone?	
Could the manufacturing of the product harm the environment?	
Could recycled materials be used to manufacture the product?	

Q2   When designing a product you must be sensitive to the people you're designing for.
      State three possible factors that you could take into consideration.

Q3   This poster has received lots of complaints.
      Why do you think lots of people found the
      text offensive?

Q4   A car air freshener is to be packaged and marketed for women. The air freshener is made
      from wood which has been soaked in fragranced oils. The packaging consists of a
      transparent vacuum formed container, which has been glued onto a cardboard background.
      A slogan is to be printed on the cardboard background, "For women drivers only!".
      Give two reasons why this product could be socially and environmentally unacceptable.

Environmental Issues

Q1 Explain why softwoods are more environmentally friendly than hardwoods.

Q2 What resource issue must people be aware of when manufacturing products made from plastics?

Q3 Why should we be careful when disposing of old or unwanted products?

Q4 The sentence below states how recycling can help the environment. Copy and complete it using words from the box below.

Reusing or .... products can save ...., energy and .... resources.

non-renewable	money	recycling

Q5 What does this symbol mean?

Q6 The arrows in the symbol in Q5 represent three things (the 3 R's). What are they?

Legal Issues

Q1   What is a trademark?

Q2   Why do trademarks exist?

Q3   If someone else used your trademark what could you do?

Q4   What is a patent?

Q5   Outline the Trade Description Act of 1968.

Q6   What do the letters COSHH stand for and what does it do?

Q7   Draw the COSHH symbol.

Q8   The British Standards Institute (BSI) checks products, and states whether they have been manufactured to a good standard. Those that pass are given a 'Kitemark'. Draw a picture of the BSI Kitemark.

Q9   If a product has the CE mark on its packaging, what does it mean?

Labels

Q1 List three laws which state what type of information must be displayed on product labels.

Q2 List two examples of safety considerations that could be displayed on a label for the benefit of the consumer.

Q3 The Food Labelling Regulation of 1996 states that foods must display certain information on their labels. List five things that should be included on all food labels.

Q4 Some foods display 'Nutritional Information' in the form of a table. What information would you expect to see in the table?

Q5 What should the label on this product say in order to meet the Food Labelling Regulations of 1996?

Warning — this bag of peanuts may contain traces of nuts...

Rant coming.......... You've just got to know the three laws that cover product labelling. AND, you've got to know what each of the laws says. Learn, learn, learn, learn, learn, learn, learn.

CAD

Q1   What does CAD stand for?

Q2   Give an example of where, in industry, CAD might be used.

Q3   Copy the table below and write in it four advantages and four disadvantages of using CAD.

Advantages	Disadvantages

Q4   Name two types of CAD software.

Q5   How can CAD be advantageous when designing a product, if a
manufacturing company has two sites, one in England and one in Australia?

CAM

Q1   What does CAM stand for? Describe what it is, and how it works.

Q2   Name two machines that could be used with CAD software to manufacture products.

Q3   Copy the table below and write in it three advantages and three disadvantages of using CAM.

Advantages	Disadvantages

Q4   The machine below is a CNC cutter and plotter.

a) What does CNC stand for?

b) Describe how this machine would work in practice.

DTP and Photo-Editing Software

Q1   What does DTP stand for?

Q2   State three reasons for using DTP.

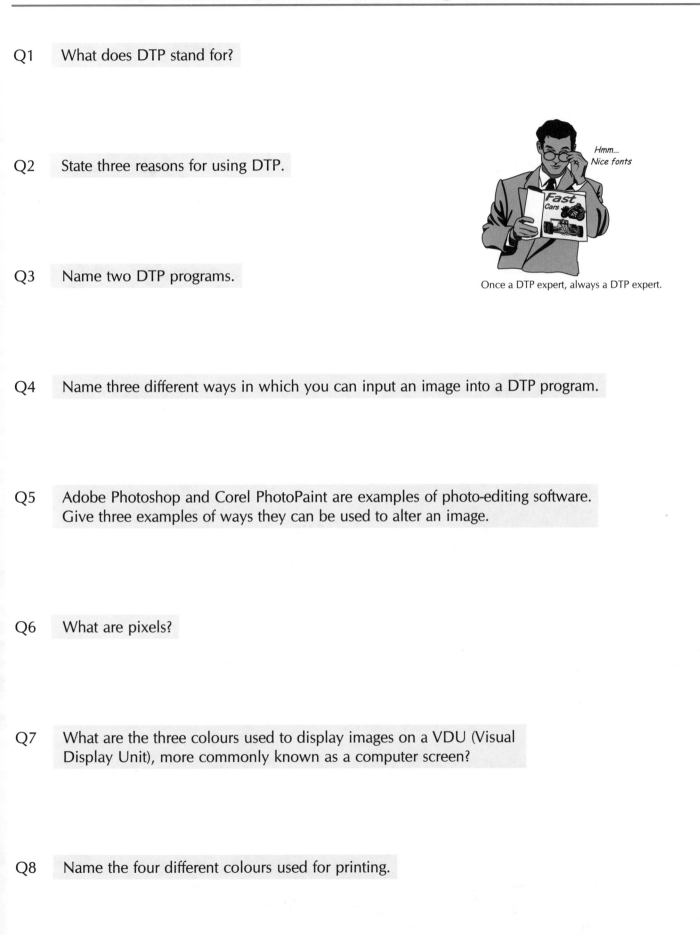

Hmm...
Nice fonts

Fast
Cars

Once a DTP expert, always a DTP expert.

Q3   Name two DTP programs.

Q4   Name three different ways in which you can input an image into a DTP program.

Q5   Adobe Photoshop and Corel PhotoPaint are examples of photo-editing software.
      Give three examples of ways they can be used to alter an image.

Q6   What are pixels?

Q7   What are the three colours used to display images on a VDU (Visual
      Display Unit), more commonly known as a computer screen?

Q8   Name the four different colours used for printing.

ICT in Industry

Q1 Name three places where people use ICT as part of their everyday lives.

Q2 Name two advantages of using ICT in the workplace.

Q3 Name two disadvantages of using ICT in the workplace.

Q4 Why is the electronic transfer of data useful for companies with separate sites?

Q5 What does the term 'Electronic Data Interchange' (EDI) mean?

Q6 Name two other ways in which data can be electronically transferred.

Q7 Tele-conferencing allows meetings to take place around the world at the same time in different locations. Write a couple of sentences to explain briefly how it works.

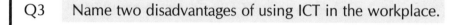

ICT in industry — on desks, every hour when people get a bit bored...
Learn all this stuff about ICT in the real world — it'll prove to the examiners that you can apply theoretical stuff to real-life situations. And it's good practice for the next 40 years of your life.

Section Five — The Wider World

Health and Safety

Q1   Copy and complete the following sentence
using **some** of the words from the box below.

The Health and Safety Act 1974 was passed to ensure that .... provide a ....
working environment and that they use .... to help reduce the risk of ....

> flooding   safety signs
>
>   friendly   safe
>
>   employers   waterbombs
>
> employees   jam
>
>   accidents

Q2   What are the basic responsibilities of a factory inspector?

Q3   If a D&T teacher was to start a new project using chemicals or dangerous machinery,
what must he/she do to identify and minimise any risks during the lessons?

Q4   Write down all the different safety signs and features you can see in your D & T workshop.

Q5   Write four safety rules that you should always follow when using machinery.

Q6   Write two safety rules that you should follow after you've finished handling materials.

Think — is it safe, or dangerous? Safe, or dangerous?

This'll help you remember safety rules: Andy Squashed His Terrible Goat. That stands for — **A**pron,
Sleeves, **H**air, **T**ies, **G**oggles. Bet that picture makes sense now. Well, a little bit more sense anyway
— or maybe it's just falling off the nonsense cliffs and slamming into the insanity beach below.

Systems and Control

Q1   Below are three stages and three descriptions relating to systems.
Write the stages down the page in the order they would happen in a
system, and then copy out the correct description next to each one.

PROCESS

INPUT

OUTPUT

the finished product
changing inputs to produce the required products
the tools, materials, energy, labour or information needed

Q2   Give an example of an input device.

Q3   Give an example of a process.

Q4   Give an example of an output device.

Q5   Copy and complete the table below by describing how to
make a piece of toast using the systems process.

Input	Process	Output

Q6   Copy and complete these sentences to explain what
feedback is. Use the words from the box to fill in the gaps.

Feedback allows a system to be .... is monitored,

and the information is used to change the ...., or adjust the

production process. Feedback is shown as a .... on a flow chart.

inputs   loop   output   corrected

Euch. You can have
this feedback...

Mechanisms

Q1   Mechanisms involve motion. Name the four types of motion pictured below.

a)   c)

b)   d)

Q2   What is the name of this mechanism?

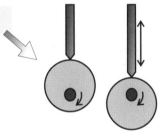

Q3   There are three types of levers. Each lever consists of a **load**, an **effort** and a **fulcrum**. For each of the products below, identify the type of lever and annotate with an arrow the load, effort and fulcrum.

Q4   Copy the spider diagram below and complete it by naming three types of mechanism.

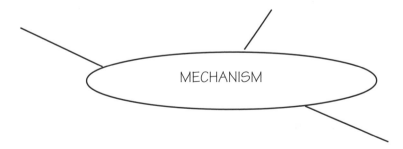

MECHANISM

Q5   Name a type of mechanism that is able to do all of the following:

    i)   transfer energy   ii)   reverse direction   iii)   make lifting heavy loads easier

Scale of Production

Q1   What phrase is used to refer to the quantity of the product that is to be manufactured?

Q2   Jobbing production is when a single product is made.
      Describe a disadvantage of this in terms of skills and labour.

Q3   Give an example of a product that would be made using the jobbing production method.

Q4   Batch production is where you make a specific quantity of a product.
      State an advantage of using this method of production.

Match Production

Q5   What does the term 'down time' mean?

Q6   What method of production involves the manufacture of a product on a large scale?

Q7   Name the method of production that involves uninterrupted, non-stop production.

Q8   What does JIT stand for and what does it mean?

Eating too many pies leads to mass production...

You can't get out of this — it's classic exam material. You need to learn *all* the details about *all* the different scales of production so that they roll off your tongue faster than a mouldy sprout.

Commercial Products and Packaging

Q1 a) Name a method that could be used to make the plastic packaging inside a new mobile phone box.

  b) Name a method of production that could be used to make the cardboard box.

  c) Name a process that could be used to print the surface graphics onto the box.

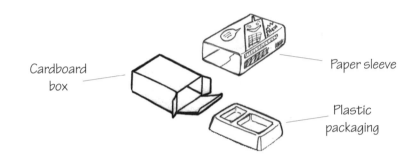

Cardboard box

Paper sleeve

Plastic packaging

Q2 Name two ways in which a design could be applied to a T-shirt.

Q3 What manufacturing process is usually used to make the plastic top of a milk bottle?

Q4 Name a plastic that could be used for the blow moulding method of manufacture.

Q5 Copy and complete the sentences below to describe what colour registration is. Use the words from the box to fill in the gaps.

  Colour registration marks allow printers to check that the .... they

  used are in the correct .... and have the right ....

colours	densities	positions

Q6 What are crop marks?

Printing Methods

Q1 Letterpress printing is a form of relief printing. What does this mean?

Q2 Letterpress printing is used for printing large amounts of monochrome text. Write down what the word 'monochrome' means.

Q3 Roughly how many prints of a copy could be produced using this method?

Q4 What method of printing has a printing plate is in the form of a rubber or plastic cylinder (as opposed to a plate, which is used for letterpress printing)?

Q5 Give two examples of products that would ideally be printed using this method.

Q6 Copy out this description of gravure printing, choosing the correct words or phrases from the pair given.

> Gravure is an **expensive** / **inexpensive** printing process.
> It's used for **low quality** / **high quality** products such as **wallpaper** / **magazines**.
> The printing plate is **etched** / **painted**, meaning the image is
> **raised above** / **lower than** the surface of the plate.

Q7 What size of print run would you expect to make if you were using gravure printing?

Q8 Lithography works on the principle of two substances not mixing together.

   a) What are these substances?   b) Explain briefly how lithography works.

Surface Effects and Photocopiers

Q1   What is the name of the cutting, scoring and folding process used to make packaging?

Q2   Below is a packaging design that could be used for die cutting. It shows score lines, cutting lines and gluing tabs. What is this design more commonly known as?

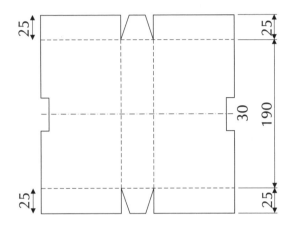

Q3   Describe what the process of embossing involves.

Q4   On the covers of some publications there is a shiny metallic finish to the title or logo of the book. What method is used to achieve this effect?

Q5   A sign is to be printed advertising a car boot sale in your local park. The signs will be stapled to trees and placed around the park so that people going for walks will see the sign. How could the signs be protected from the rain?

Q6   What are the four main types of varnishing techniques that could be applied to printed work?

Q7   Paper is the main material used when photocopying, but you can also photocopy onto other materials. Name two materials other than paper that you can photocopy onto.

Production Methods and Barcodes

Q1   Give a brief description of how CAD and CAM are used to produce graphic products.

Q2   Give two examples of products that can be made easily using a CAM machine.

Q3   Write down an advantage of using devices such as jigs, templates and moulds.

Q4   Give one example of what you might use each of the following for (in manufacturing):

        a)   jigs

        b)   templates

        c)   moulds

Q5   What piece of equipment would you use to convert photographs or hand-drawn images into a computer file?

Q6   Give two advantages of using barcodes.

Barcodes are dead useful — but a bit woolly...

These are some of the new and fancy methods industry uses to improve systems and speed up the production process. Ah, isn't D&T fun... (sigh). Anyway, these questions cover topics that'll be in your exam. Which is why they're in this book. If you can't do them you need to learn your stuff.

__Packaging and Waste__

Q1   State three reasons for having packaging.

Q2   What can manufacturers add to packaging to prevent
customers messing about with the product?

Q3   Name two materials that would be ideal to package a product
to prevent it from being damaged during transportation.

Q4   What is the main reason for the deterioration of food products?

Q5   What sorts of packaging prevent this type of deterioration?

Q6   What do manufacturers do to their packaging to entice consumers to buy their product?

Q7   Name three things you would expect to see on the packaging of a product.

Q8   List three things that the public and people in industry
can do to minimise unnecessary and waste packaging.

Q9   A company sells foil-wrapped chocolates in a vacuum formed plastic tray,
inside a cardboard box, covered in cellophane. It's designer has been asked to
come up with a more environmentally friendly way of packaging the chocolates.
List as many ways as you can of improving the current packaging method.

Q10 Name three packaging items that could be reused many times.

What a waste of pizza...

Q11   What does recycling mean?